BLUEPRINT

English Key Stage
Copymasters

Jim Fitzsimmons

Rhona Whiteford

Stanley Thornes (Publishers) Ltd

BLUEPRINTS – HOW TO GET MORE INFORMATION

The following titles are currently available. New titles are being added every year.

Topics
Assemblies
Writing
Science 5–7 Teacher's Resource Book
Science 5–7 Pupils' Copymasters
Science 7–11 Teacher's Resource Book
Science 7–11 Pupils' Copymasters
English Key Stage 1 Teacher's Resource Book
English Key Stage 1 Pupils' Copymasters
English Key Stage 2 Teacher's Resource Book
English Key Stage 2 Pupils' Copymasters
History Key Stage 1 Teacher's Resource Book
History Key Stage 1 Pupils' Copymasters
History Key Stage 2 Teacher's Resource Book
History Key Stage 2 Pupils' Copymasters
Environmental Education Key Stage 1
Environmental Education Key Stage 2

Geography Key Stage 1 Teacher's Resource Book
Geography Key Stage 1 Pupils' Copymasters
Geography Key Stage 2 Teacher's Resource Book
Geography Key Stage 2 Pupils' Copymasters
Technology Key Stage 1
Technology Key Stage 2
Health Education Key Stage 1 Teacher's Resource Book
Health Education Key Stage 1 Pupils' Copymasters
Health Education Key Stage 2 Teacher's Resource Book
Health Education Key Stage 2 Pupils' Copymasters
Maths Key Stage 1 Teacher's Resource Book
Maths Key Stage 1 Pupils' Copymasters
Maths Key Stage 2 Teacher's Resource Book
Maths Key Stage 2 Pupils' Copymasters

Books may be bought by credit card over the telephone and information obtained on (0242) 228888. Alternatively, photocopy and return this FREEPOST form for further information.

Photocopiable

Please send further information on BLUEPRINTS to:

Name _____

Address_____

_____

_____

Postcode_____

To: Marketing Services Dept., Stanley Thornes Publishers, FREEPOST (GR 782), Cheltenham, Glos. GL53 1BR

First published in 1992 by:
Stanley Thornes (Publishers) Ltd
Old Station Drive
Leckhampton
CHELTENHAM GL 53 0DN

A catalogue record for this book is available from the British Library.

ISBN 0–7487–1172–4

Typeset by Tech-Set, Gateshead, Tyne & Wear
Printed in Great Britain at the Bath Press, Avon

CONTENTS

In this book there are 124 photocopiable copymasters linked to many of the activities in the Teacher's Resource Book. Where the copymasters are referred to in the text of the Teacher's Resource Book there are instructions on how to use them. They are referred to by number in the Teacher's Resource Book by this symbol . The copymasters reinforce and extend activities in the Teacher's Resource Book and provide opportunities to record activities and results in an organised way. When the children have completed these copymasters they can be added to workfiles or used as exemplar material in pupil profiles. You may also wish to use completed copymasters as a resource for your assessments.

Storyboard

Characters	Location

Time/weather	Opening

Main event	Main event

Ending	Other notes

News report

Telephone calls

I've been listening

Today's topic is . . .

We heard about it
a) on the radio ☐
b) from our teacher ☐
c) on the tape. ☐

I want to ask these questions . . .

Planning an outing

Where are we going?			
When are we going?	Date		
	Leaving time		
Will we need special equipment?	Yes		No
What?			
Will we need food?			
Will we need money?			
Are we staying overnight?	Yes		No
If so, what do we need?			
How are we getting there?			
What will we do when we get there?			
What time will we leave?			
What time will we arrive home?			
Will we need to be met?			
How will we pay for the trip?			

Reasons

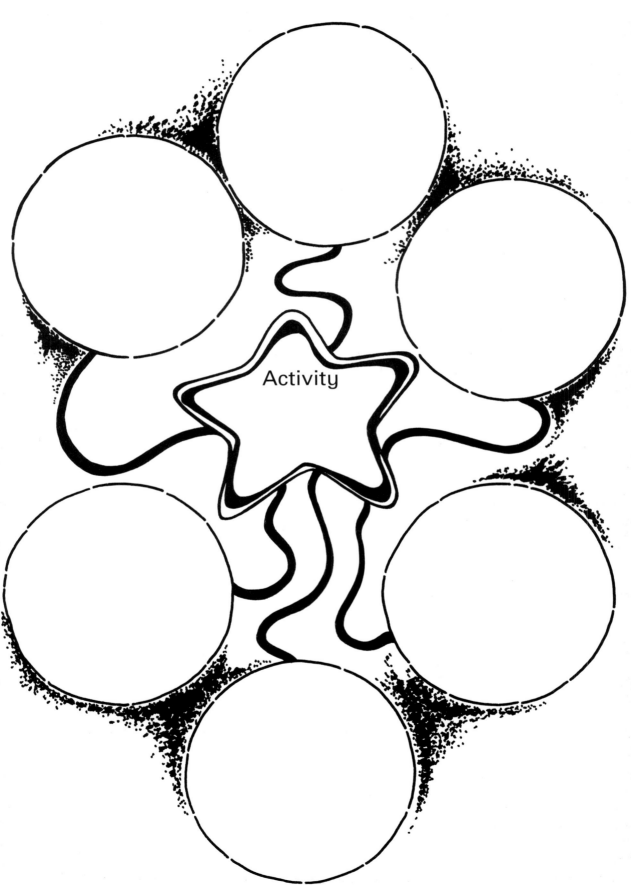

Activity

Checklist

What is needed?

What is its purpose?

Who will use it?

When will it be used?

Where will it be sited?

Where is it to be made?

What materials are needed to make it?

Have we got them?

How much will they cost?

Who will make it?

How long will it take?

Lip-reading

What do you think?

Work with a friend. Draw yourselves (head and shoulders will do) and write what you think about this.

Holiday choice

Work with a partner and draw yourselves in the picture frames.

Each pick the holiday you prefer and write down why it appeals to you.

In the news

Work with a friend. Draw yourselves (just head and shoulders) and write what you think of this incident shown on the news. Make notes of your impressions and feelings.

Describing what happened

What can I remember about the event?

What did I enjoy most?

What did I enjoy least?

What did I find most interesting?

How did I feel before the event?

How did I feel after it?

What do I think other people would like to hear about the event?

Would I like to do it again?

Look at it another way

Could these characters be seen in a totally different way?
Discuss what they may be like and make notes.

Snow White

Aladdin

Rumpelstiltskin

My feelings

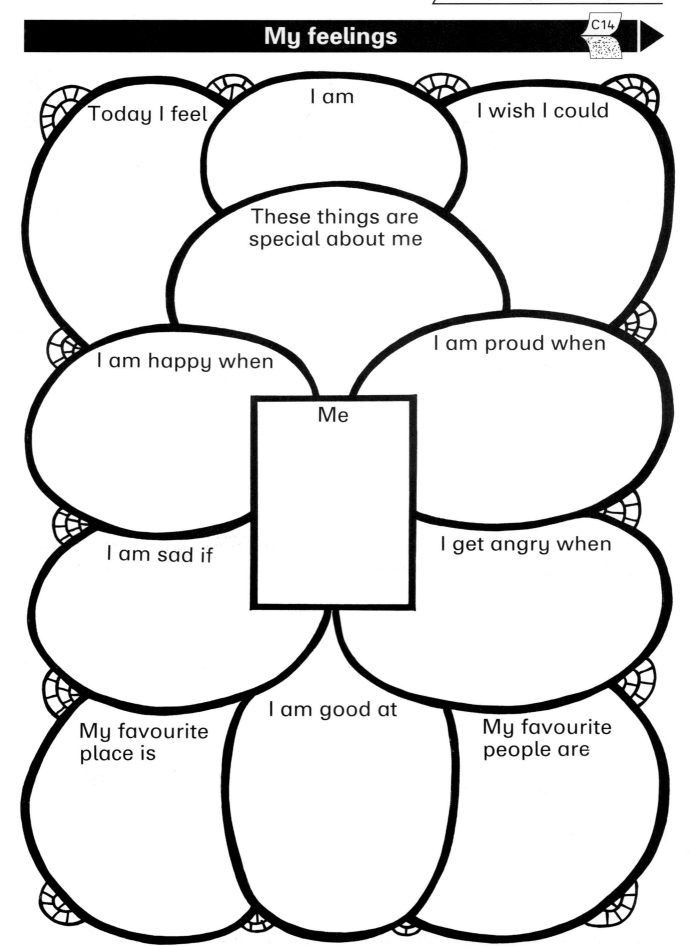

Today I feel

I am

I wish I could

These things are special about me

I am happy when

I am proud when

Me

I am sad if

I get angry when

My favourite place is

I am good at

My favourite people are

Lost and found

C16

Programme planner

C17

Order of items	Presenters	Technical staff

Form of presentation: live/recorded/both

Type of presentation: quick report, feature programme

Age of audience

Programme subject

Length of programme

Programme title

News area

Item . . .	Item . . .	Item . . .

Talking heads

Book of the month

My selection of good books

1st

2nd

3rd

Book report

Title _____

Author _____

This book is about _____

_____

_____

_____

_____

_____

I would/would not recommend this book

because _____

_____

_____

_____

Date _____ Name _____

Storyboard

Setting/location

Main event

Opening

Main event

Characters

Significant details

Ending

How is the story made?

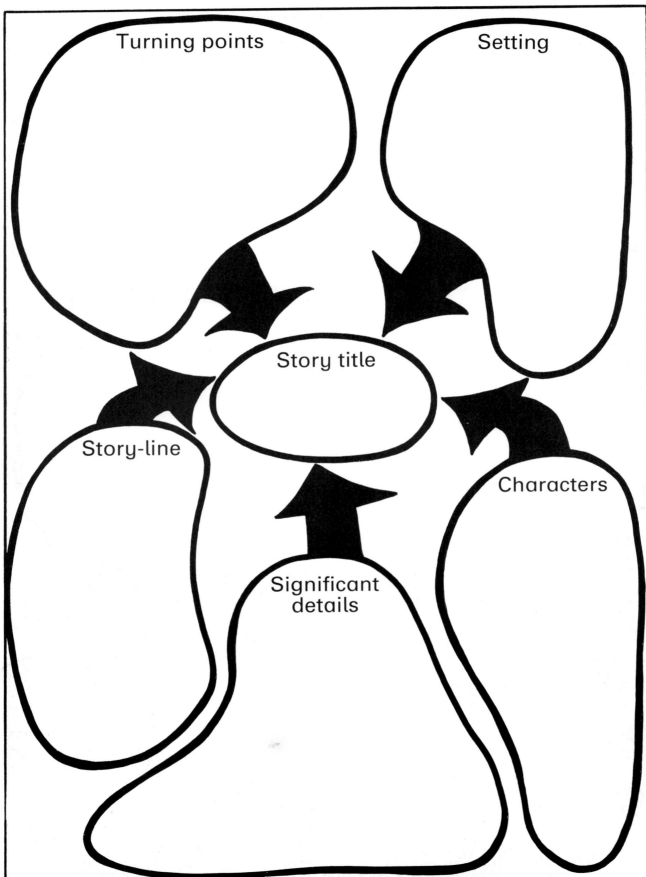

The beginning

Main event

Ending

Favourite character

C24

I like _____

_____

because the character is:

funny ☐   exciting ☐

clever ☐   magical ☐

scary ☐   good ☐

beautiful ☐   kind ☐

other

I like the stories because

Comparing characters

Name of character: _____

Title of book:

kind	
honest	
brave	
generous	
handsome	
friendly	

cruel	
dishonest	
cowardly	
greedy	
ugly	
fierce	

lives in	eats	is a

Other information _____

_____

_____

_____

_____

_____

_____

Crystal gazing

What happens next? _____

_____

_____

_____

_____

_____

_____

_____

_____

_____

_____

What happens next?

Dean and Jenny hurried down the road.
It was getting dark and the shopping Dean
carried was heavy. Jenny switched on her torch as
they turned into End Lane, an unlit country road with
few houses. The wind howled loudly. As they got to
the darkest part of the lane the headlights of a car
appeared at the end of the lane and moved quickly
towards them. They couldn't hear the engine as the
wind blew the sound over the fields.
They panicked and scrambled onto the grass verge as
the headlights seemed to be on top of them. Dean
dropped the bag and grabbed Jenny quickly. She
screamed wildly as the car ran right over. . .

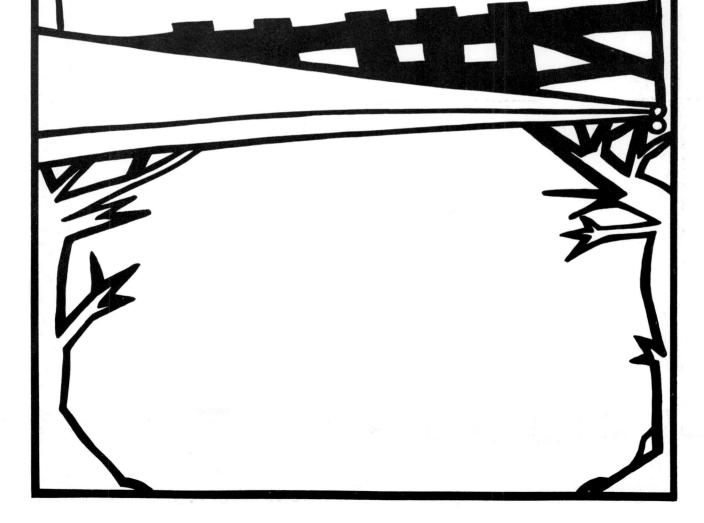

My own story

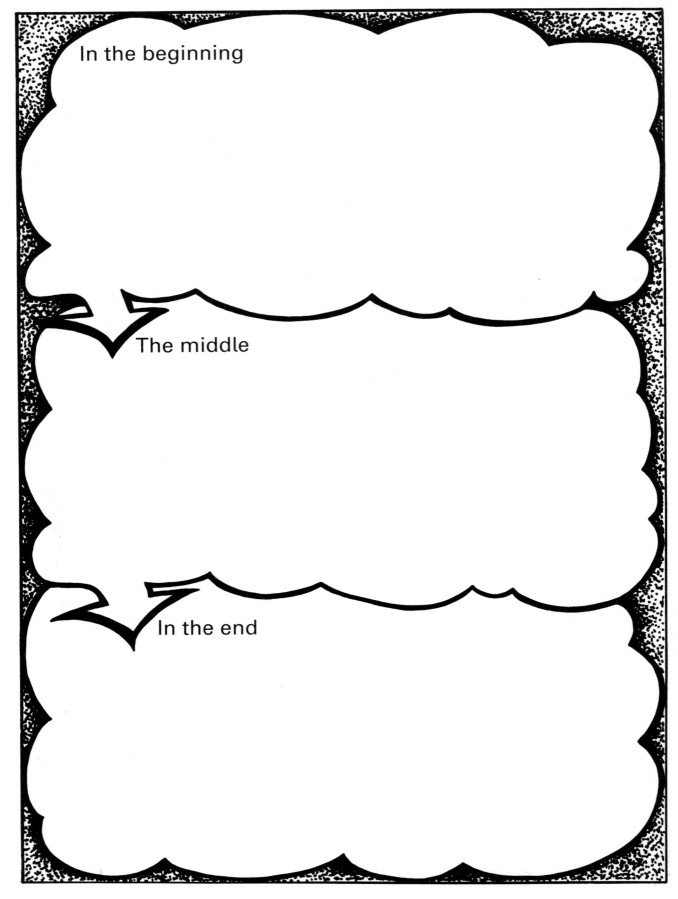

In the beginning

The middle

In the end

Charlotte's Web

Table of contents

Here is the contents list from a book about space and space travel:

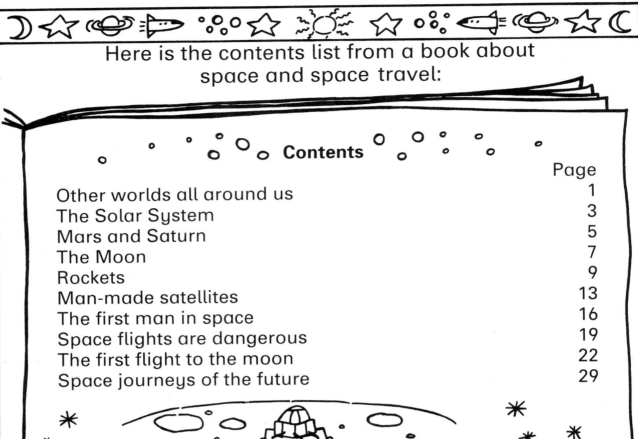

Contents

Where would you find the answers to these questions in the book? Write the name of the section and the page number on which it starts.

1 What is the date of the first landing on the moon?
2 What is the distance from the Sun to Venus?
3 What makes Saturn different from the rest of the planets?
4 What are the "seas" on the moon?
5 Name three dangers of space flight.
6 Who was the first person to set foot on the moon?
7 What is a satellite?
8 Why is a rocket built in two or three parts?
9 Give the names of the planets in our Solar System.
10 Why is Mars called the red planet?

Index list

Index

A
Agriculture 7
Aqueducts 22
Artesian wells 28
Atmosphere 10
Avalanche 9

B
Ball float 44
Body water content 26
Building materials 3, 32
Buoyancy 5, 7

C
Capillarity 26, 32
Casting 14
Chloride sodium 26
Clouds 27
Clothing 41
Corrosion 20, 21
Crystals 27, 44
Currents 32, 33

D
Dams 42, 43, 44
Dead Sea 6
Delta 30
Density 6, 8, 12
Desalination 22, 23
Distilled water 6, 9
Drains 24
Drinking water 22
Drought 7

E
Effluent 24, 25
Erosion 30, 44
Evaporation 6, 10

F
Filter beds 23
Flood plain 42
Fluoride 63
Fog 27
Frost 41

G
Geothermal power 20
Geysers 21
Glacier 27
Gulf stream 15

H
Hailstones 23
Humidity 40
Hydroelectric power 26

I
Ice 15
Iceberg 17
Industry 40–1

K
Kaplan turbine 42

L
Lagging 38
Limestone 28

M
Mass 45
Meander 30
Mineral water 28, 29
Molecules 10, 16

Information about these topics can be found on:	Page no
Evaporation	
Buoyancy	
Geysers	
Icebergs	
Drinking water	
Corrosion	
Atmosphere	
Hailstones	
Dams	
Aqueducts	
Erosion	
Delta	
Hailstones	
Artesian wells	
Fluoride	
Gulf stream	
Crystals	
Fog	
Humidity	
Avalanche	
Clouds	

Finding information in an encyclopedia

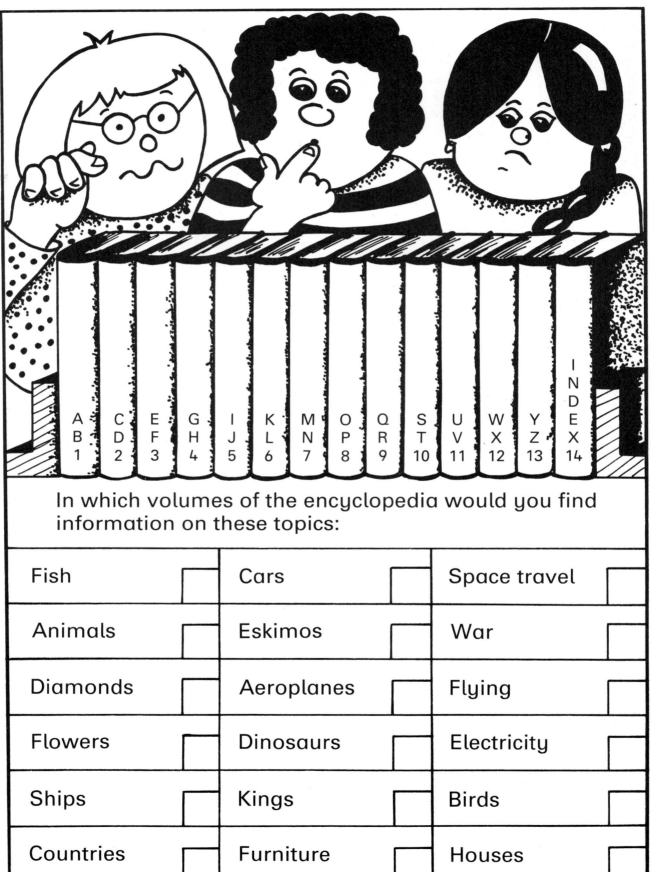

In which volumes of the encyclopedia would you find information on these topics:

Fish		Cars		Space travel	
Animals		Eskimos		War	
Diamonds		Aeroplanes		Flying	
Flowers		Dinosaurs		Electricity	
Ships		Kings		Birds	
Countries		Furniture		Houses	

Choosing the right book

Write the title of the book most likely to contain answers to these questions:

1	What colour is a robin's egg?
2	How many players are there in a basketball team?
3	Who was the first American in space?
4	Which king was on the throne in 1675?
5	How do you crochet and knit?
6	Name Queen Victoria's husband.
7	Who invented the car?
8	Which is the largest desert in the world?
9	How do you make a sponge cake?
10	What was the leader of 100 Roman soldiers called?

Voices

My space craft is damaged. I need to return home or I shall die. You must help me. I urgently need some Lythian crystals to re-energise my power source. Already I can feel the life force draining from me. It's becoming difficult to breathe . . .
help me . . .help me . . . aargh . . .

I am the dragon Zofor. I demand that you give me twenty sheep to eat. If you refuse I shall destroy your homes with one blast of my fiery breath. I shall wait until midday. If I have not received an answer, beware!

Now here's the news that's going around, a brand new sound has just hit town. Stamp your feet and start to clap. All join in the classroom rap. Just keep that rhythm good and strong and keep on rappin' all day long.

A personal response

Story-line

Characters

Setting

Subjects

Form

Title

Illustrations

Writing style

What held my interest:

My favourite bit

This is my favourite part.

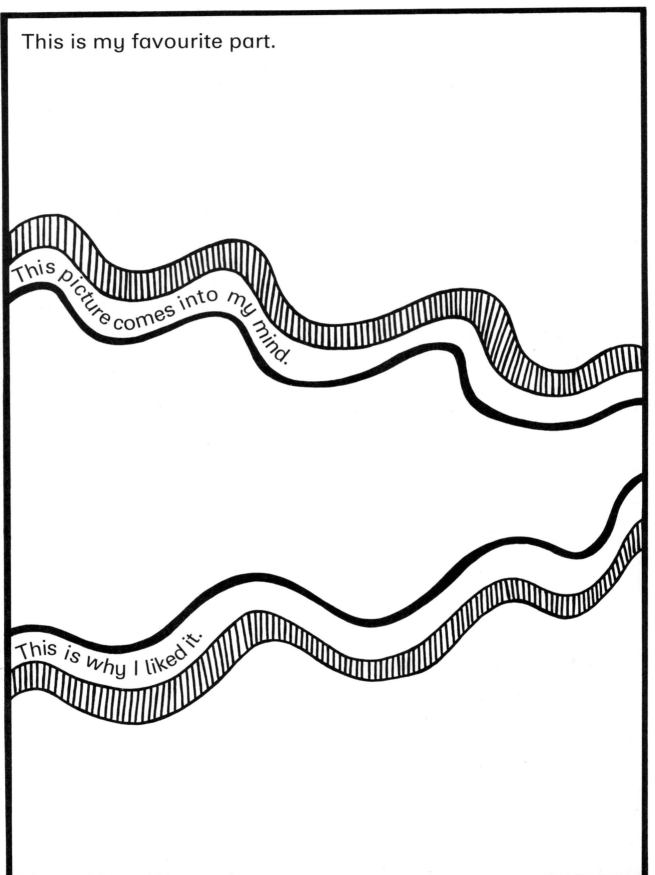

This picture comes into my mind.

This is why I liked it.

Night life

Darkest clouds in blackest night,
no stars to shed a friendly light.
Instead the hard and jagged flare
of neon signs, electric glare.
Wet roads swimming, rivers of rain,
sheets of water, a shooting pain
of cold.
Cardboard city, sodden damp;
tapping shoes to the taxi rank.

I think . . .

Prediction exercise

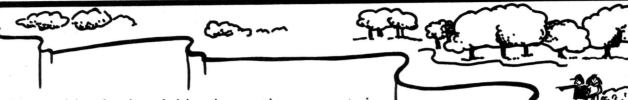

Ahmed looked quickly down the mountain track. They were still being followed but he and Amina were well prepared with supplies, maps and a radio. Their enemies did not know the land and the twins had a good start.

At the foot of the rock face, two humanoid creatures stood quietly watching the children scrambling along the high track on the ridge. Their eyes met and a greenish light seemed to glow between them as they communicated without expression on their faces. The tallest one began to shimmer like a neon light, then faded and disappeared. His partner turned to look up at the ridge.

Amina and her twin stopped. They could take the forest track which was slow, or abseil over the cliff edge, or lie in hiding for a while. They did not see the green glow materialise in the trees behind them . . .

Write or draw what happens next.

Once more, Ultraman!

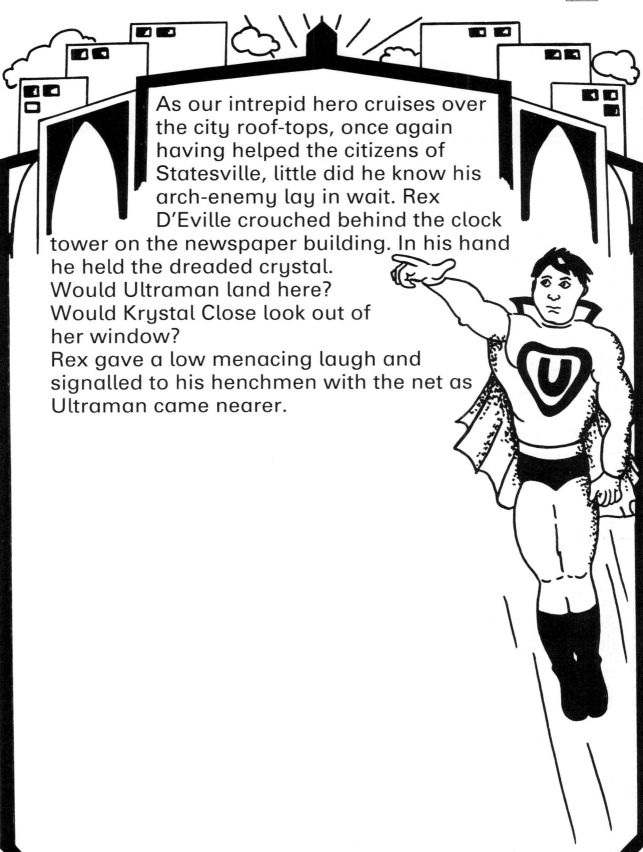

As our intrepid hero cruises over the city roof-tops, once again having helped the citizens of Statesville, little did he know his arch-enemy lay in wait. Rex D'Eville crouched behind the clock tower on the newspaper building. In his hand he held the dreaded crystal.
Would Ultraman land here?
Would Krystal Close look out of her window?
Rex gave a low menacing laugh and signalled to his henchmen with the net as Ultraman came nearer.

The secret of Dark Towers

Zendo paused at the heavy oak door. It was unbarred but smoke was curling in long tendrils from beneath it. So, the fire had spread. He looked up at the window. He could just reach it though getting through it would be a struggle and the moat below was deep and cold. It would be possible to swim the moat if he did not land on one of those terrible metal spikes in the water. Zendo gripped the rough stone of the wall. Behind him came the slithering sound of the creature's long tail sweeping the floor. It paused and sniffed the air, growling. Zendo didn't wait any longer. He . . .

. . . reached up to the high window and climbed skilfully. He squeezed himself through and, gripping the lintel, he looked down. The dark waters of the moat shimmered in the moonlight and a shaft of light caught one of the cruel spikes. It glinted wickedly in the water. The creature's growl could now be heard above him on the battlements. Zendo swung himself out and, clinging like an insect to the rough walls, he climbed slowly . . .

. . . down and lowered himself into the water without a splash. He waited as the beast sniffed and snorted above him and then seemed to move off. Then, as a dark cloud covered the moon's piercing light, he swam noiselessly across. Safely on the bank, he whistled softly to his horse waiting by the postern gate. The animal came quickly, its eyes wide with the terror of the night. Mounting swiftly, he was away. But what of the secret of Dark Towers? It waited there on the battlements, its green eyes following him.

Put in the missing words

C41

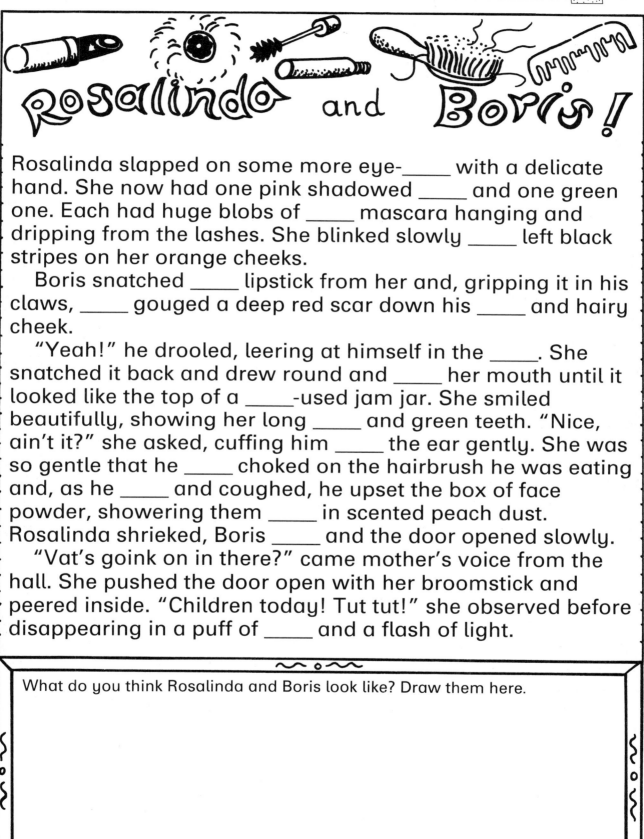

Rosalinda and Boris!

Rosalinda slapped on some more eye-_____ with a delicate hand. She now had one pink shadowed _____ and one green one. Each had huge blobs of _____ mascara hanging and dripping from the lashes. She blinked slowly _____ left black stripes on her orange cheeks.

Boris snatched _____ lipstick from her and, gripping it in his claws, _____ gouged a deep red scar down his _____ and hairy cheek.

"Yeah!" he drooled, leering at himself in the _____. She snatched it back and drew round and _____ her mouth until it looked like the top of a _____-used jam jar. She smiled beautifully, showing her long _____ and green teeth. "Nice, ain't it?" she asked, cuffing him _____ the ear gently. She was so gentle that he _____ choked on the hairbrush he was eating and, as he _____ and coughed, he upset the box of face powder, showering them _____ in scented peach dust. Rosalinda shrieked, Boris _____ and the door opened slowly.

"Vat's goink on in there?" came mother's voice from the hall. She pushed the door open with her broomstick and peered inside. "Children today! Tut tut!" she observed before disappearing in a puff of _____ and a flash of light.

What do you think Rosalinda and Boris look like? Draw them here.

The Dewey system

000–099 *General Works* including encyclopedias, journalism, libraries, etc.

100–199 *Philosophy* (critical views of life and the universe).

200–299 *Religion*

300–399 *Social Sciences* (the study of people and their organisations), including economics, law, education, occupations, customs, etc.

400–499 *Language* including grammar and dictionaries.

500–599 *Sciences* including mathematics, astronomy, physics, chemistry, biology, zoology, botany, etc.

600–699 *Technology* including engineering, medicine, agriculture, business, computers, television, transport, etc.

700–799 *The Arts* including architecture, sculpture, painting, music, photography, sports and recreation, etc.

800–899 *Literature* including great novels poetry, plays and criticism of literature.

900–999 *General Geography and History.*

A In which of the ten main groups would you find books with the following titles:

1	Life Beneath the Waves	
2	Stamp Collecting	
3	Dairy Farming	
4	How to Play Football	
5	Great Rivers of the World	
6	The Reign of Henry VIII	
7	The Solar System	
8	Punctuation	
9	How Television Works	
10	Advanced Mathematics	

B Make up a list of ten other book titles with one for each of the Dewey classifications.

Where will I find?

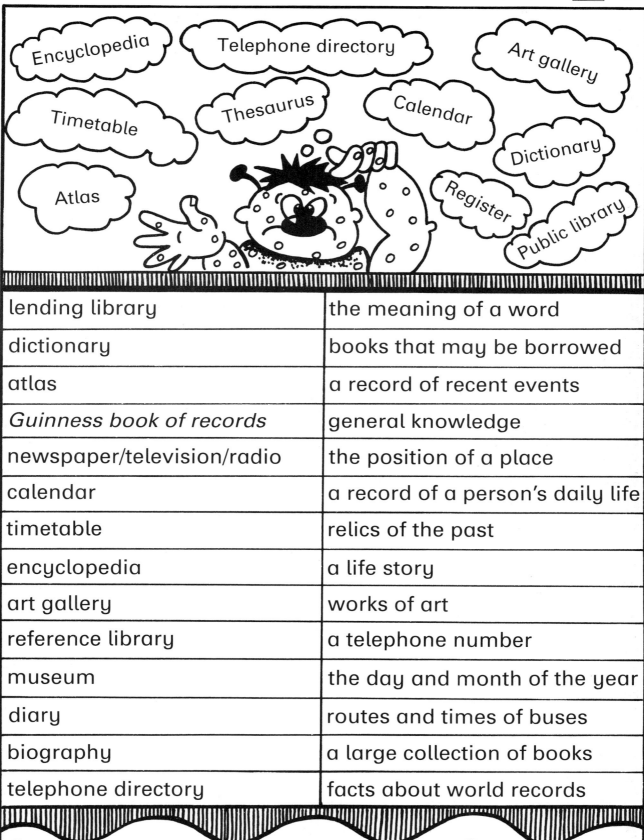

lending library	the meaning of a word
dictionary	books that may be borrowed
atlas	a record of recent events
Guinness book of records	general knowledge
newspaper/television/radio	the position of a place
calendar	a record of a person's daily life
timetable	relics of the past
encyclopedia	a life story
art gallery	works of art
reference library	a telephone number
museum	the day and month of the year
diary	routes and times of buses
biography	a large collection of books
telephone directory	facts about world records

Spot it

To find the answer to these questions, glance very quickly at the picture above. Try to find and write down the answers very quickly.

1	How many boats can you see?
2	How many flags can you see?
3	How many people are there?
4	Is the sun shining?
5	How many people are in the rowing boat?
6	How many birds can you see?
7	How many people are in the water?
8	How many dogs can you see?

Take your pick

Each of these objects appears in one of the small pictures below.

Look at them carefully and then glance at the pictures below to see just how quickly you can spot each item.

Use this space to match them up.

object								
picture								

Telephone directory

MANCHESTER Smith A 743

Smith Albert, 14 Station Road 061 331 5174
Smith Doris, 5 Union Terrace 061 275 5693
Smith Eric, 6 Garswood Road 061 492 4055
Smith Frederick, 8 Hamilton Road 061 492 5037
Smith Gladys, 142 Green Lane...061 113 6294
Smith Henry, 45 Ivy Crescent 061 432 6231
Smith Joan, 27 Union Street 061 442 3412

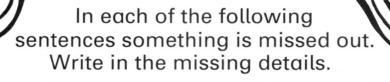

In each of the following
sentences something is missed out.
Write in the missing details.

1 Joan Smith's telephone number is 061 _____ 3412

2 Doris Smith lives at 5 _____ Terrace.

3 Albert Smith lives at _____ Station Road.

4 Frederick Smith's telephone number is 061 492 _____.

5 Henry Smith's telephone number is 061 _____ 6231.

6 _____ _____ lives at 142 Green Lane.

7 Eric Smith lives at 6 _____ _____.

8 Albert Smith's telephone number is 061 _____ _____.

9 _____ _____ lives at 27 Union Street.

10 Gladys Smith's number is _____ _____ 6294.

Scanning

- Look at each item in the list below and see which sport is mentioned.

- Remember the name of the sport and glance rapidly down the index until you find it.

- Write down the number of the page the information can be found on.

Index

	Page
Badminton	6
Canoeing	28
Cycling	7
Diving	13
Football	3
Hammer	15
Javelin	10
Marathon	19
Netball	23
Rugby	32
Skating	45
Swimming	12
Tennis	38
Volleyball	43
Wrestling	2

		Page
1	How to throw the hammer	
2	Cycling equipment	
3	The size of a football pitch	
4	Different ways of diving	
5	The height of a volleyball net	
6	Balancing a canoe	
7	Holds in wrestling	
8	The rules of rugby	
9	The history of the marathon	
10	How to throw the javelin	
11	The number of players in a netball team	
12	Figures in skating	
13	Different strokes in swimming	
14	Famous tennis players	
15	Marking a badminton court	

Search reading

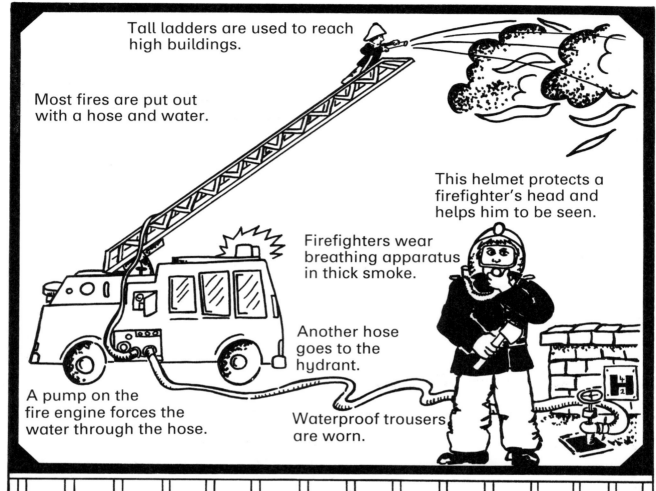

Tall ladders are used to reach high buildings.

Most fires are put out with a hose and water.

This helmet protects a firefighter's head and helps him to be seen.

Firefighters wear breathing apparatus in thick smoke.

Another hose goes to the hydrant.

A pump on the fire engine forces the water through the hose.

Waterproof trousers are worn.

Search this picture to find the answers to these questions.

1. What do firefighters use to put out most fires?
2. Why do firefighters wear helmets? Write two reasons.
3. What tool is the firefighter holding?
4. What would it be used for?
5. When would the breathing apparatus be used?
6. What does the pump on the fire engine do?
7. What does the letter on the roadside sign stand for?
8. Find some books about firefighting and write two or three interesting things about the job.
9. Why is an extending ladder used?
10. Would you like to work as a firefighter? Give a reason for your answer.

C49

THE TIMES

TODAY'S DATE   CIRCULATION   PRICE

Fact or opinion

C50

If the sentence is a fact write "fact" in the box at the side. If you think it is an opinion write "opinion" in the box. Underline the words in the sentences which show that it is an opinion.

1	Susan is the prettiest girl in our school.	
2	John is 1.83 metres tall.	
3	My dad's car is the shiniest and smartest car in town.	
4	The antique clock is the finest clock you can see anywhere.	
5	John and Peter are twins.	
6	Peter is more handsome than John.	
7	My garden contains roses, carnations and honeysuckle.	
8	My garden is the most beautiful one in the village.	

For and against

Fact: Peter won the boys' high jump.

A Peter was very lucky to be high jump champion because his main rival had an off day, and Peter is not that good.

For | Against

B As expected, Peter won the high jump championship even though his main rival did not jump as well as usual. The margin of defeat was very great and Peter's jumping was excellent.

For | Against

Fact: The school play was performed on the 4th April.

A The school play was performed really well by a strong cast. The sets and costumes were really great.

For | Against

B The school play was rather boring and far too long. The sets were dreary and the acting was wooden and poor.

For | Against

Advertisement

Fascinating facts

Take an encyclopedia and open it up at any page. Scan the page and see if anything catches your eye. Look out for something really fascinating. When you have found something, copy it out carefully. Be sure to make accurate notes of where you found the information so that other people can look it up for themselves.

Source: Volume number: page:

Research

Use encyclopedias, non-fiction books, magazines or any other source to find out information about famous people or inventions.

Famous people

Name: _____

Claim to fame: _____

_____

_____

_____

_____

_____

Famous invention

Name of invention: _____

_____

Name of inventor: _____

_____

Use of invention: _____

_____

Date and place of invention: _____

Illustration

Can you draw a picture to illustrate this?

There was an old man with a beard
Who said "It is just as I feared
Four larks and a wren
Two owls and a hen
Have all built their nest in my beard."

Edward Lear

Can you write an appropriate text for this picture?

Books

C56

BOOKS

These are the books that I have read this month:

_____

_____

_____

_____

_____

_____

_____

_____

_____

_____

_____

Name: _____

Date: _____

Awards 1

Reading award

This is to certify that

_____

has read

_____

Signature: Date:

I have read

This is to certify that

_____

has read

_____

Date:

Signature:

Awards 2

Sentences 1

My friend has curly hair.

She crunches gobstoppers for lunch.

She laughs a lot.

She is great fun.

She has only three teeth left.

Make up five sentences about your friend. Start each one with a capital letter and end it with a full stop.

1 _____

2 _____

3 _____

4 _____

5

Draw a picture of your friend.

Sentences 2

Here are some sentences and phrases mixed up. Pick out the five sentences and write them with a capital letter and a full stop.

1 there are monsters in my loft
2 for my tea
3 the monsters are green and noisy
4 Mum said
5 they are slimy and slippery
6 them all out
7 we met one evening
8 if I said
9 one night
10 we had a good chat

1	
2	
3	
4	
5	

Now try to use all the phrases to make complete sentences which make sense. You will need to add some more words.

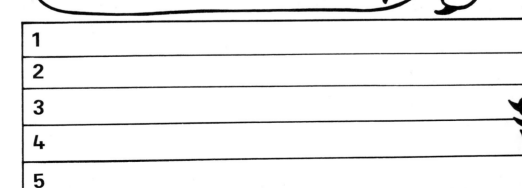

1	
2	
3	
4	
5	

Sentences 3

I have mixed up these sentences for you! You will never be able to put the words in the right order and get them to make sense.

Put capital letters this end.

1 tea. slime I in put green my

_____

2 know would yours. some in like you I

_____

3 Tea cold should awfully taste and bitter.

Put full stops this end.

I have zapped all the full stops from this passage. Try to put them in. Try hard.

It was a cold and moonlit night As the clouds drifted across the moon an owl hooted In the trees a noise could be heard A soft whispering became excited chatter Two small figures darted from the bushes and sped across the forest Leaping and shouting the goblins headed for the cave

Doing words 1

Action words

Can you find the doing words in these sentences?

1   The greedy things ate everything in sight.
2   Six wild horses galloped past them.
3   The rockets blasted off into space.
4   They floated gently on the water.
5   The car sped down the road.

Underline the doing words.

Here are some sounds and the things that made them.
Can you match them?

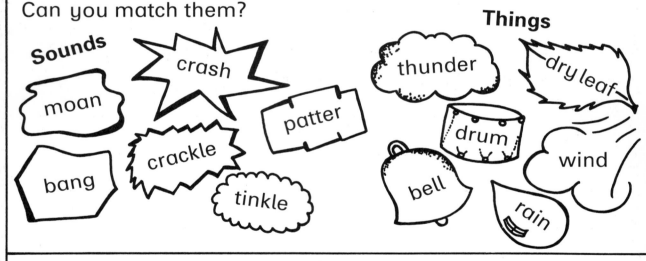

Sounds

moan
crash
patter
bang
crackle
tinkle

Things

thunder
dry leaf
drum
wind
bell
rain

Down on the farm it is noisy.
Write the sound each animal makes.

bark   cluck   grunt   bray   low   mew

Doing words 2

C65

There are two doing words in each sentence.
Can you find them? Underline each one.

1 Eat your tea and then wash the pots.
2 Jump in the bath and wash yourself.
3 The dog leaped into the pond and swam away.
4 His owner dragged him out and took him home.
5 The dog barked all the way and the man laughed.

These children are all doing different things.
Write a sentence about each one.

Danny   Wesley   Jacie   Sam   Kim

1
2
3
4
5

jumping
running
playing
swimming
kicking
bathing
leaping
hopping
batting
skipping

Write three sentences about the things you like to do best.

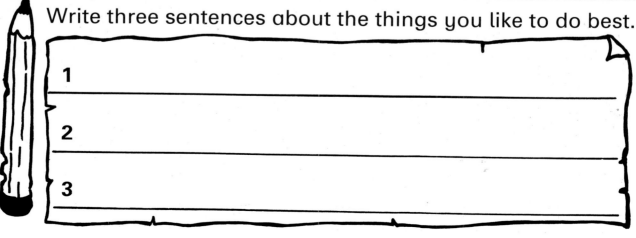

1
2
3

Doing words 3

Here are some doing words.
Put them into sentences.

write
dry
wish
speak
pour

1   I like to _____ stories.
2   Stand in the corner and don't _____.
3   I _____ I could have chips for tea.
4   _____ the water into the teapot.
5   Wash your hands and then _____ them.

aimed   standing   slipped
threw   tied   fell   tumbled   felt

Write three sentences about this picture.
Try to use two doing words for each one.

1 _____

2 _____

3 _____

Nouns 1

Read the beginning of this story and underline the nouns.

The door was heavy and took some pushing to open it. Slowly it moved. The children peeped through the gap and before them was a wonderful garden. Outside it was dark but inside the garden the sun shone, birds sang, bees hummed and it was warm. Flowers of all kinds grew everywhere. The children stepped inside and the door closed behind them.

Pick a noun.

cat

Read the sentences and pick which noun you think fits. Write it in.

1 The little _____ leaped gracefully over the gate.   cat/frog
2 The slimy green _____ sat very still.   toad/fish
3 It was dark and _____ were flying.   bats/birds
4 _____ raced across the sky.   birds/clouds
5 An _____ hooted in the night.   owl/car

Underline the nouns in this collection of words.

row   ran   rabbit   dog   help   food

bone   insect   table   took   chair   pen

Nouns 2

These two sorts of nouns have got mixed up. Sort them out.
Put a capital letter where it is needed.

Proper Nouns

Tuesday

tuesday   telly

sam   august

ben

lolly   dog

jones   cat

man

smith

bench   teacup

Common nouns

telly

The colours are common nouns.
Can you unjumble these names
and colour the quilt?

yreg   erango   ylloew   der

thwie   neerg   rulpep   lbue

This is wrong.

Rewrite it correctly putting in any capitals needed.

mr. slipup,
mistake st.,
wrongton,
messyshire

Put your name and address here.

Look carefully

Q = Question
A = Answer

Q	How many people can you see who look scared?
A	
Q	Who looks most interested in the ghost?
A	
Q	Can you see anyone hiding?
A	
Q	What has the old man dropped?
A	

Can you write a short story about this picture? Where are they? What happens next?

Read carefully

C70

Something to chew over
A croc came out of the jungle,
And waddled down our way.
He ate for lunch with a mighty crunch
Three lads and their bags and a little bunch
Of grapes, on a sunny day.

He licked his chops and blinked the eye
That was left in his scarred old face.
He stretched his jaws in a mighty yawn
But there wasn't a trace
Of his lunch that sunny day.

We yelled and wailed and leaped away
From the swing of his thrashing tail.
He gave us a grin,
Said "Thanks for the din!"
And was gone from the sunny day.

Q Where did the crocodile come from?
A

Q What did he eat for lunch?
A

Q Was the crocodile old or young?
A

Q What was the weather like that day?
A

Q Was the crocodile sorry to have eaten the lads?
A

Q = Question
A = Answer

Questions

Some of these people are asking a question. Read carefully and if they are, put a "?" at the end of what they say to show it is a question.

Are you feeling well.

Did you play out last night.

Have you had dinner yet.

You can play with me tonight.

You look quite poorly.

1

2

3

Draw yourself and someone who looks after you.

Today is the day he or she cannot say "No!"

Ask three questions. Think carefully.

Don't forget this:

Sorting sentences

Read the sentences and put them in order by writing their letter in the boxes below. The first sentence is f so that goes in box 1 and so on.

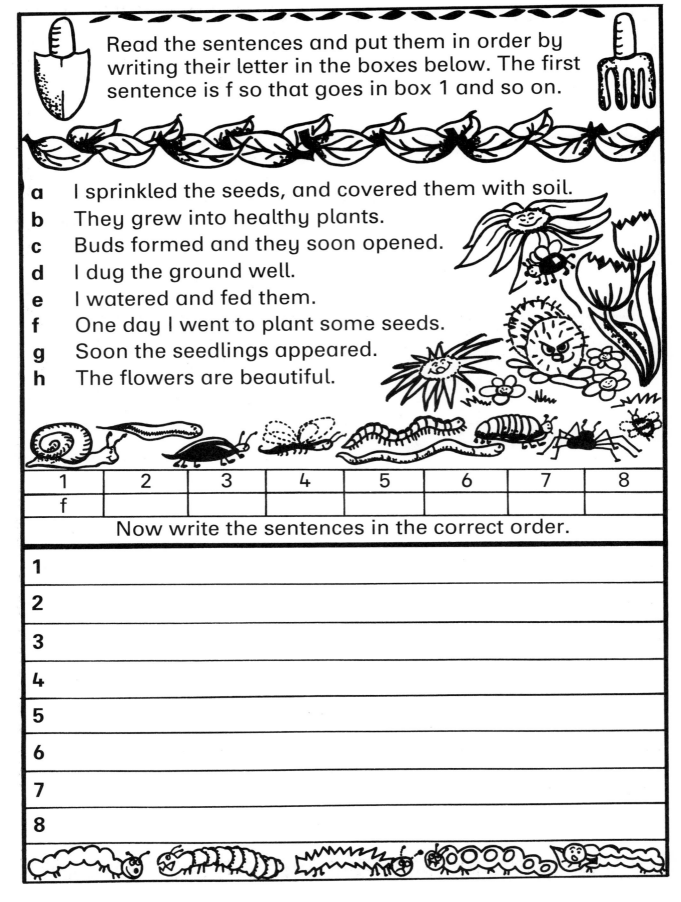

a   I sprinkled the seeds, and covered them with soil.
b   They grew into healthy plants.
c   Buds formed and they soon opened.
d   I dug the ground well.
e   I watered and fed them.
f   One day I went to plant some seeds.
g   Soon the seedlings appeared.
h   The flowers are beautiful.

1	2	3	4	5	6	7	8
f							

Now write the sentences in the correct order.

1	
2	
3	
4	
5	
6	
7	
8	

Joining sentences

1	He couldn't take part.	He was too old.
2	Becky was very tired.	She went to bed.
3	The sun was shining brightly.	Tom was still cold.
4	Reeaz saw how late it was.	He ran home.
5	Sally did a handspring.	She did a somersault.
6	I was very nervous.	I went to the dentist.
7	I had my supper.	I went to bed.
8	I answered all the questions.	I was the winner.
9	We were late.	We still caught the train.
10	Sarah spilled her drink.	She must mop it up.
11	It was raining very hard.	We enjoyed walking.
12	He could not play football.	He had lost his boots.

although   soon   before   after   and   since   because

yet   which   next   when   so   then   but   who

Descriptions

C74

Notes

Name

Male/Female

Size/Height

Build

Shape

Colour of skin

Dress

Voice

Age

Shape of face

Any unusual features

General behaviour

My friend

Guess who

The picture

The description

It's...   by

Describing words

Match the nouns with an adjective and draw the result.

nouns

egg-cup   bucket

feet

hat   sausage

hair   jelly

balloon   hands

adjectives

metal   brown   wet

fluffy

furry   straight

floppy   slimy

wobbly

green   hairy   red

woolly

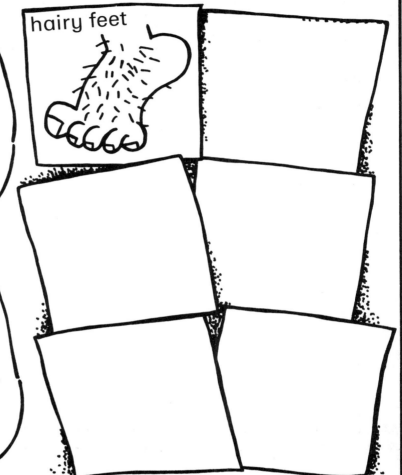

hairy feet

Pick one or two adjectives to describe these pictures. Write your choice underneath.

beautiful   neat   sparkling   awful   fabulous   glittering

good   lovely   safety   ghastly   great   wonderful

_____ sunglasses

_____ shoes

_____ helmet

Adjectives 1

Here are some words which describe people. Draw a picture of yourself and a friend or a story character. Then pick three words which best describe each of you.

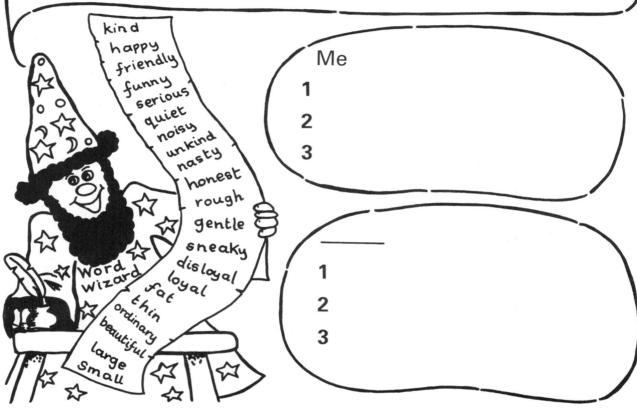

kind
happy
friendly
funny
serious
quiet
noisy
unkind
nasty
honest
rough
gentle
sneaky
disloyal
loyal
fat
thin
ordinary
beautiful
large
small

Word Wizard

Me

1

2

3

_____

1

2

3

Read this letter and underline all the adjectives you can find.

School camp 19—

Dear Pal,

This is the best holiday I have had. There is an adventure playground. I did the dangerous rope-slide today. Dave wore his knee-length shorts for everything, even bed! I can't stand the rotten food. There are burnt sausages, cold spaghetti, slimy custard and flabby bread — and that's for breakfast! I bought Joe a great kite and Sally some sticky rock.

See you soon,

me ↓

← Dave's lovely shorts!

I found ____ adjectives.

Adjectives 2

Put adjectives in the spaces.

I bought a _____ ice cream from the _____ shop. I was just walking down the _____ road when I saw a _____ _____ witch standing in front of me. She licked her _____ lips and I knew at once what she wanted. She waved her _____ wand, there was a _____ flash and when the _____ smoke disappeared the _____ ice cream was in her hands not mine. She laughed a _____ laugh and vanished.

blue   huge   kind   wrinkled   very   really   young   funny
cold   corner   magic   nasty   lovely   little   horrid
black   gigantic   wonderful   great   old   terrible   bent
delicious   cracked   silver   blinding   terrific   purple

Can you use any of these words to finish the sentences below? Pick two adjectives for each.

1 There was a _____ _____ pudding for dinner.

2 Our teacher is a _____ _____ person.

3 I've got a _____ _____ friend.

my friend

4 I wrote a _____ _____ story today.

What did you say?

Pick one of the following adjectives or use one of your own to complete what the children are saying.

bad   happy   flashing   bored   silly   happy
interesting   good   nice   glum   boring   delicious
loud   great   fantastic   awful   wonderful

Adverbs 1

Match verbs with adverbs and write them together in the stars.

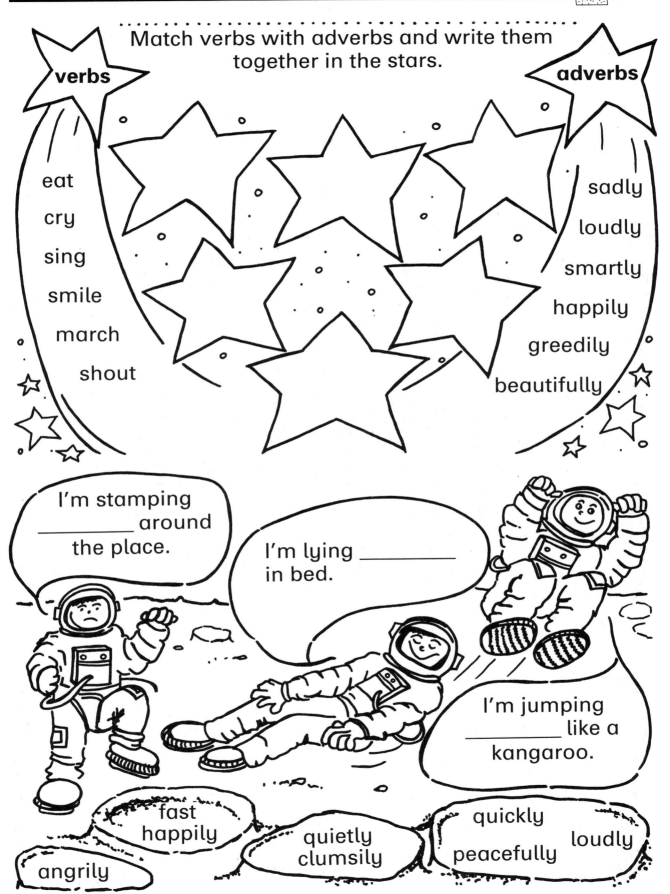

verbs

eat
cry
sing
smile
march
shout

adverbs

sadly
loudly
smartly
happily
greedily
beautifully

I'm stamping _____ around the place.

I'm lying _____ in bed.

I'm jumping _____ like a kangaroo.

fast
happily

angrily

quietly
clumsily

quickly
peacefully
loudly

Adverbs 2

Can you think of adverbs to make these sentences more interesting?

Use your dictionary to check spellings.

The burglar climbed _____ in through the window.

The tortoise walked _____ across the lawn.

The lion roared _____.

The cakes were baked _____.

Rain fell _____ all night.

Stars twinkled _____ in the sky.

Settings

Ways to start a story

It all started when . . .
One day, not too long ago . . .
Long ago in the mists of time . . .
It was a dark and dismal night . . .
We were alone in the house and . . .
Once when the world was young . . .
I'm going to tell you a tale about . . .
This is a story I heard long ago . . .
It was a bright early morning in summer when . .
The Autumn mists gathered early and the
night was growing dark when . . .
In the beginning . . .
Once upon a time . . .
Tonight . . .
When I was very young . . .

Ways to end a story

. . . and so it was all over.
. . . it had finished, at last.
. . . and now we could all have a well-earned rest.
. . . we had supper and went to bed, tired but happy.
. . . the horror was over and we were all safe.
. . . and they all lived happily ever after.
. . . there was home at last. They had made it!
. . . so it all turned out all right in the end.
. . . and it was a wonderful way to end things.

The reward

It was a damp and chill Autumn evening and the street lights were dim. Mr Johnson walked slowly, worried in case he fell on the slippery pavements. Rusty pulled at the lead and whimpered, wanting to be off to the park. The traffic rushed by in the misty light making it difficult to cross the road, so the old man stopped and waited.

Just then a stray dog, seeing Rusty, barked from the park gates opposite. Rusty leaped forwards in greeting and pulled the lead from Mr Johnson's weak hands. He was off, bounding through the traffic to the park.

"Rusty! Wait!" called the old man, terrified for the dog's life. He reached to grab the lead but slipped and fell heavily on the pavement.

It was two days later that Satish saw the article in the paper. It was about the lost pet and how anxious Mr Johnson was to find Rusty. "He's the only family I have now," the old man had said. Mr Johnson had sprained his ankle in the fall. "A £50 reward to anyone who brings him back", said the article.

Satish had found a dog, a rusty coloured pup, lost in the park. He had it with him now and he loved it already. It was his only real family too. £50! What a reward! The dog licked his hand. He had to think very carefully . . .

Storyboard

characters	place
time	main events
opening	ending

Classified advertisements

C88

CLASSIFIEDS

Captions

Capital letters

Rewrite this address putting in capital letters.

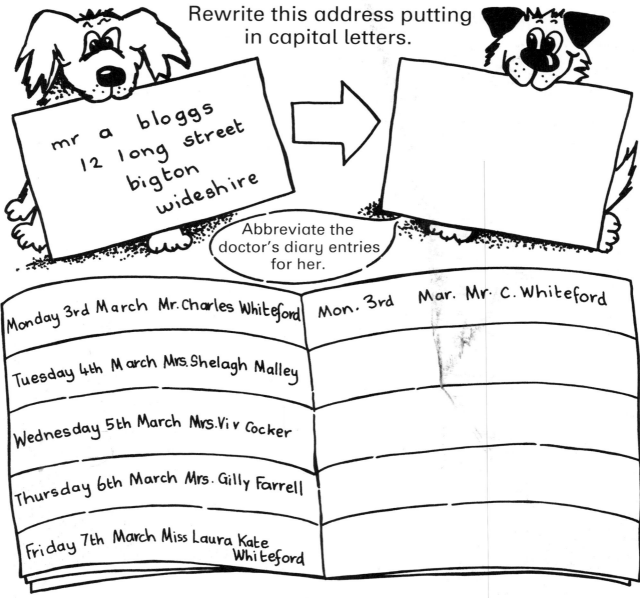

mr a bloggs
12 long street
bigton
wideshire

Abbreviate the doctor's diary entries for her.

Monday 3rd March Mr. Charles Whiteford

Tuesday 4th March Mrs. Shelagh Malley

Wednesday 5th March Mrs. Viv Cocker

Thursday 6th March Mrs. Gilly Farrell

Friday 7th March Miss Laura Kate Whiteford

Mon. 3rd   Mar. Mr. C. Whiteford

What do these abbreviations stand for?

A.A.	R.A.F.
B.A.	R.N.
R.S.P.C.A.	etc.

Can you write the abbreviations for these words?

Doctor	Smock Street
Saint Helens	Mistress
Mister	Captain

Full stops

Some writing needs full stops and some does not.

> Write a list of your favourite foods.

> Lists do not need them.

school camp

dear pal, the adventure playground at wonky towers was really great there was a death slide that was 20 metres above the ground next to it there was a scramble net that went across a gorge before it went dark we played hide and seek in the caves in the morning we are going swimming see you soon,

> Can you put capital letters and full stops in this letter? Use a coloured pencil or pen.

How many abbreviations of metric measurements can you find? They do not need full stops after them.		km – kilometre

Write out ten abbreviations which need full stops.									
H.M.S.									

Questions

Draw your favourite TV or pop star in this crowd of fans. Write in the speech bubbles the sort of questions you think your friends might ask the star.

Turn these sentences into questions by tagging a question mark onto the end.

I can get home myself.

It's early.

The bus should come soon.

It's not far.

It won't take long.

Turn the full stop into a comma.

 Turn these indirect questions into direct ones.

He asked what time it was.	
She asked what size it was.	
He wanted to know what to do.	
She wondered what was for dinner.	

Exclamation marks

What could these people be saying?
Write something that needs an exclamation mark.

Draw one of your family here and write in the speech bubble three exclamations that they often say.

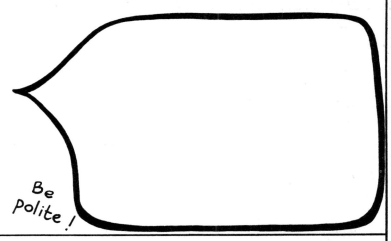

Be Polite!

Put an exclamation mark or a question mark on these sentences. Sometimes a single word can be a sentence.

Help me.   How old are you.   Stop.   Come here.

What a mess.   Hello.   I don't believe it.

Who did it.   Quick march.   Get out.

Commas

C94

Lists Put commas in these sentences which contain lists.

1 Dave soon learnt to run skip jump and leap.

2 The house was warm bright comfortable and welcoming.

3 We need brushes paint water paper and cloths.

Dear Bert,

Write a letter to a friend to arrange a holiday. You will need to decide what things you will be taking. Put commas and the word "and" in your lists.

Marking off This is done with names and words with meanings of their own.

1 Well David what do you call this?
2 Look out Gina the wall's wobbly.
3 Yes I would like double chips.
4 I can do it myself thanks Mum.
5 No I don't want to go to bed Dad.
6 I would agree son but it's late.

Speech

Put in the missing capital letters in these sentences.

1 Dad said, "it's time you were in bed."
2 I replied, "oh, Dad, let me stay up."
3 "sorry," he answered, "it's time to go."
4 I was really cross and shouted, "blow!" as I went upstairs.
5 Dad sighed and said, "kids today!"

Think of six quiet verbs of saying and six loud ones.

 Arrange this sentence in two other ways:
"I think TV is really great!" exclaimed Joey.

Write this out using speech marks and setting it out correctly.

Did you hear about the musician who spent all his time in bed? asked Sue. No replied Alec. Well he wrote sheet music laughed Sue, slapping her knees.

Planning for the audience

Planning for ~ the audience ~

Audience	Age group	General preferences	Suggestions for writing

Date: Researcher/s:

Sequencing

Letter

Invitation

Poetry

C100

Sentences

Here are some simple sentences.
Underline the subjects in red
and the predicates in blue.

1	My mum loves watching telly.
2	Come inside quickly Freddy.
3	The jolly green giant squashed my house.
4	I love chips and chocolate.
5	Head over heels went Dad!

Think of a subject for these predicates.

You can use adjectives!

1	Into the pot went	
2		loves strawberries and custard.
3		stamped and screamed for ages.

Think of a predicate for these subjects.

1	The awful, spotty thing	
2		Auntie Nelly the fierce.
3	The classroom clock	

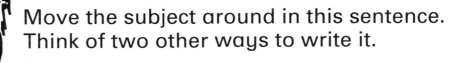

Move the subject around in this sentence.
Think of two other ways to write it.

| Big Robbie strode happily down the Glen. |
| 1 |
| 2 |

Layout

The first engines Engines give things power to work Long ago there were no engines people had to do all the work themselves they rowed boats they fetched water in jugs but they used the power of horses for travelling Water wheels were one of the first kinds of engine water gave the power to turn a large wheel and this wheel turned other wheels Windmills were used for grinding corn and for pumping water the wind blew the sails the sails turned the wheels the first steam engines were used to work pumps in mines because the mines were often flooded the pumps sucked water through pipes out of the mine One of the first steam engines to pull a passenger train was called the Locomotion the engine went very slowly and a man had to ride in front with a red flag to tell people to move out of the way Steam engines were used to drive all kinds of machines steam coaches and cars were very big and clumsy steam traction engines were used in the fun fair to drive the merry-go-round and the steam organ In old steam ships the engines turned huge paddles to drive the ship through the water later steamships had propellers to drive the boat along

Verses

1 There are big waves and little waves green waves and blue waves you can jump over waves you dive through waves that rise up like a great water wall waves that swell softly and don't break at all waves that can whisper waves that can roar and waves that run at you running on the shore.

Eleanor Farjeon
© David Higham Associates

2 Far from the loud sea beaches where he goes fishing and crying here in the inland garden why is the seagull flying here are no fish to dive for here is the corn and the lea here are the green trees rustling hie away home to sea fresh is the river water and quiet among the rushes this is no home for the seagull but for the rooks and the thrushes pity the bird that has wandered pity the sailor ashore hurry him home to the ocean let him come here no more high on the sea-cliff ledges the white gulls are trooping and crying here among rooks and roses why is the seagull flying

R.L. Stevenson

Research into writing use

C104

Type of writing	SE/NSE	Purpose of writing	Place used

I see what you mean

Garage mechanic

"From the X-ray I can see that there is a greenstick fracture of the left tibia and I think it may need exploratory surgery."

Ambulance woman

"I have been busy preparing the Crème Vichyssoise, Scallop Chowder and Fillet de Beouf en Croûte, to be followed by the Soured Crème Flan."

TV Repair man

"A mixture of perennials and half hardy annuals which need a dappled shady site and which have some tolerance to alkaline soils will be best for this plot."

Doctor

"Sierra Two to base, over."
"Sierra Two go ahead."
"I have a male, aged approximately 40 years, Code 2, with severe head injuries and respiratory arrest. Request paramedic crew at once. Over."

Chef

"I have changed the oil filter and the carburettor. The spark plugs have also been changed and I tightened the fan belt. As a result the overall m.p.g. should be much better."

Gardener

"The microchip needs replacing on the circuit board so that tracking for the VCR and satellite dish can be altered. The vertical hold and contrast need adjusting as well."

Crossword

Here are the clues to help you guess the words.

Down
1   You do this when you know something is the truth.
2   This is someone who steals things.
3   A loud scream that starts with sh . . .

Across
1   A part of a cake
2   Grass can grow in this.
3   A girl relative, your brother or sister's child

Sounds check: consonants

th	sh	ch	fl
cr	dr	bl	st
sk	nt	nd	ff
ss	qu	ph	kn
wr	mb		

Sounds maze

C108

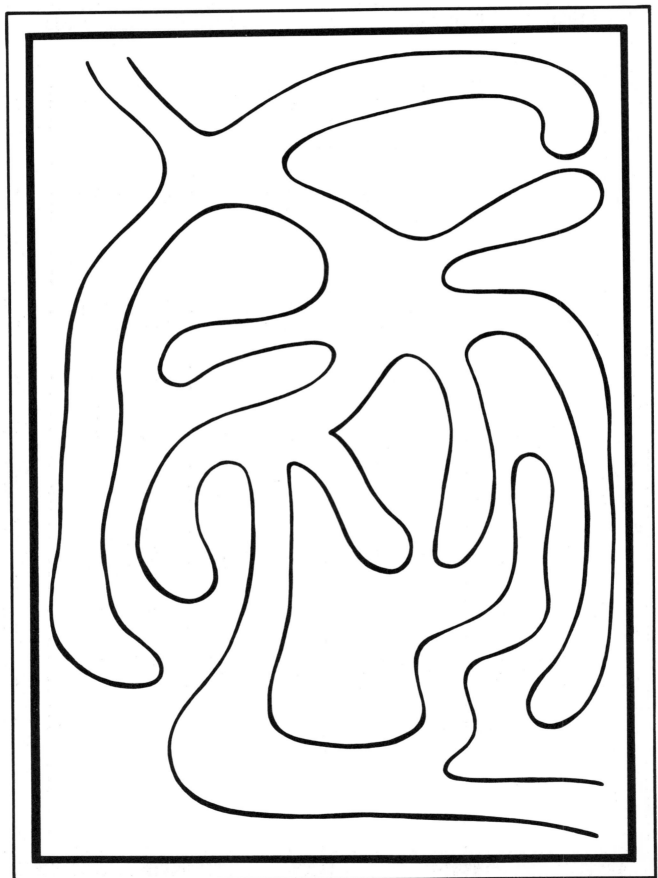

Sounds check: vowels

a	e	i	o	u	e (both short and with magic)

ai	ay	er	aw

ea (short)	ea (long)	ur	ear

ie	ey	ee	ui

oa	or	au	oo

ou	oy	ow	ew

| ar | | | |

Sounds check: letter strings

ing	ous	ion	ly
le	ies	ed	ful
dge	tch	ought	ight
aught	ves	nch	

Word families

run	laugh	hop	sing	drawing
clean	hops	runs	sit	cleaning
draws	cleaner	sings	running	singer
laughing	sitting	hopping	cleaned	hopped
drawn	sits	laughed	sat	runner
cleanest	draw	sung	singing	ran
laughter	sang	drew		

Tenses

Kelly was running down the road.

I like to eat ice cream.

Mum will pay on Sunday.

The song was sung by Neil.

I am going to town.

I shall be sunbathing next week.

The money has been stolen.

I am taking the dog to the vet.

Next week I shall see my cousin.

Peter saw the accident.

The vase was broken yesterday.

Courtney is writing a letter to his sister.

Underline the verbs: past tense in red, present tense in green, future tense in blue.

...sand sea sea sun!

Prefixes

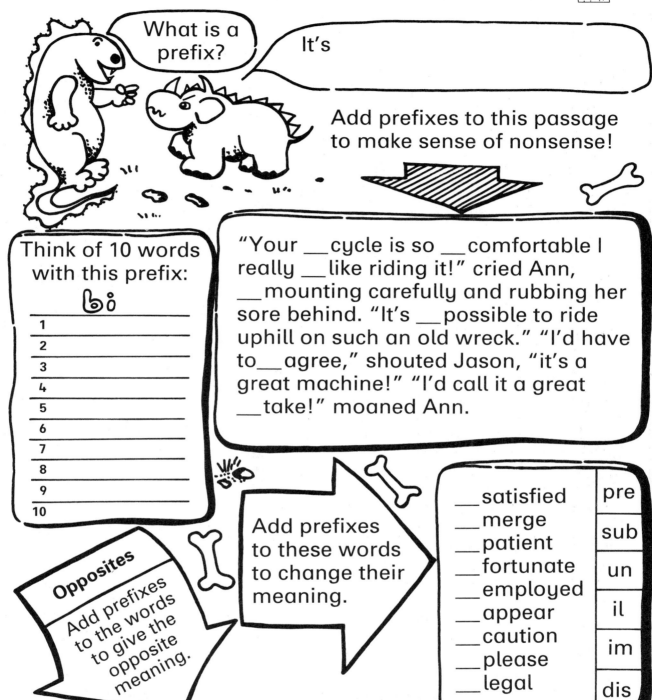

What is a prefix?

It's _____

Add prefixes to this passage to make sense of nonsense!

Think of 10 words with this prefix:

bi

1 _____
2 _____
3 _____
4 _____
5 _____
6 _____
7 _____
8 _____
9 _____
10 _____

"Your __cycle is so __comfortable I really __like riding it!" cried Ann, __mounting carefully and rubbing her sore behind. "It's __possible to ride uphill on such an old wreck." "I'd have to__agree," shouted Jason, "it's a great machine!" "I'd call it a great __take!" moaned Ann.

Opposites
Add prefixes to the words to give the opposite meaning.

Add prefixes to these words to change their meaning.

__satisfied
__merge
__patient
__fortunate
__employed
__appear
__caution
__please
__legal

| pre |
| sub |
| un |
| il |
| im |
| dis |

1 You'll have to __screw it to get it off.
2 That chair is so __comfortable I've got back ache.
3 We'll have to __roll the carpet to lay it.
4 Weighing three tonnes, the statue was __movable.
5 I was __satisfied with the bad treatment.

Suffixes

Add suffixes to these words to make adjectives.

Add noun suffixes to change these words.

care__
station__
ghoul__
fright__
light__
dark__
station__

less
ed
ful
ary
ery
ish
ness

cart__
lead__
teach__
manage__
attain__
brother__
comrade__
seaman__

er
ship
hood
ment

Spot the suffix. Underline it!

The sky was growing lighter and the air was already warmer. Soon the sun beat down fiercely on the men. They had been childhood friends and this had grown into comradeship which had endured for many years onboard ship. Jim's loyalty had never been in question, but now he needed Rick's help. He drifted into unconsciousness as he lay on the hot sand. His wound needed attention quickly and only Rick could help. They were alone, marooned, forgotten, hungry and desperate. Rick stooped to lift his friend.

Let's make sense!

Add suffixes where needed.

You will see a gild___ rose on the door.
Enter care___ and proceed quiet___ and cautious___. Content___ will be yours.

Patterns 1

Patterns 2

cccc _____ _____ _____

ℓℓℓℓ _____ _____ _____

⋀⋀⋀⋀ _____ _____ _____

⋀⋀⋁⋀ _____ _____ _____

∿∿∿ _____ _____ _____

cccc _____ _____ _____

ℓℓℓℓ _____ _____ _____

⋀⋀⋁⋀ _____ _____ _____

∿∿∿ _____ _____ _____

cccc _____ _____ _____

ℓℓℓℓ _____ _____ _____

⋀⋀⋀ _____ _____ _____

Joining letters 1

Base line joins

in ai ey kl kl

mn nt hi lm un

en ar me tr av

deep lump mine inn

hate him den liner

Joining letters 2

C118

Joining to tall letters

nt   ck   if   ef

ul   ml   at   ub

eh   et   el   nk

tell   call   silk   lift

clock   milk   tent   mill

Joining letters 3

Joining to oval letters

ic   ea   ag   ec   ad   ig

na   co   nd   lo   to   da

ng   ed   eg   ma   ha   id

ca   td   eq   iq   nc   do

each   catch   lace   hang   made

cold   cage   ladder   mace   fade

Joining letters 4

Cross joins

oi   on   ou   ow   oy

wi   wy   vi   vo   va

od   og   oa   oo   wa

oc   om   wo   vu   wd

wood hook cool violet woman

vote dog drone blood coast

van out coin one with

Joining letters 5

C121

Joining f and t

fi   fo   fr   fa   fu

finger   field   forest   fly   foot

friend   follow   fault   full   fry

Cross joins from t (optional)

tu   ti   ta   ty   tch

tub   tie   table   tyre   catch

tag   tame   time   fetch   thyme

Joining letters 6

Joining descenders with loops

ja   go   ye   ji   ga   yo

ge   ya   yi   gu   je   ju

gi   gh   gl   jo   yu   yi

glow   yacht   gun   job   jam   yes

jester   give   yellow   ghost   grand

yap   goal   jive   get   juice

pl   pa   pu   pi   ph   pt   po

bi   bo   bu   by   ba   bp bl

os   as   sit   busy   fussy   some   skies

fox   box   oxo   vixen   xylophone

zoo   zip   fuzz   zoo   zebra   zip

qu   qu   queen   foot   free   of

Writing practice